# Seeds on the go

bowmar

# Seeds on the go

by Aileen Fisher

designed and illustrated by Hans Zander · lettering by Paul Taylor

Library of Congress Catalog Card number 76-24262
International Standard Book number 0-8372-2400-4

Ripe seeds burst from their pods and popped!!

Winged seeds rode on the wind,

then

dropped!

We walked in a meadow of grass and weeds

one day when summer was making seeds,

one day when autumn was not quite here,

but plants were thinking about next year,

with seeds to scatter both far and near.

Dry seeds rattled when Skip ran past,

brown seeds scattered,

and green held fast.

7

8

Ripe
seeds
burst
from
their pods
and
popped!

9

Winged seeds rode on the wind, then dropped,

10

hidden by grass when the blowing stopped.

"If you were a seed," said Mary Lee,
"tell us what kind you'd choose to be."

12

"A dandelion seed would really suit," said Jay. "I'd ride in a parachute!

I'd ride on the wind above the clover,

14

down
to
the
old
stone fence—

and over."

15

"A poppy seed is the one I'd choose,"
Jennifer said,

16

"so I could use
that wonderful little poppy-shaker
that sprinkles seeds on a mini-acre."

"I'd be a seed in a tumbleweed," Christopher said.

"I'd roll with speed

down the meadow where men are mowing,

and somersault till the wind stopped blowing."

Brown seeds scattered as Skip dashed by.
Seed pods rattled, all ripe and dry,

20

under the hazy harvest sky.

Then Jennifer turned to Mary Lee:

"Tell us what seed you'd choose to be."

"I'd be..."
she thought as she zipped her sweater,
"I'd be...
there isn't a seed that's better...

23

We all agreed that would be unbeatable.

"Except," we giggled, "you'd be so eatable."

Then Skip came running, and dry seeds scattered.

His fur looked rumpled, and snarled and tattered.

And Jennifer wished we had some clues

to the kind of seed that a dog would choose.

Then Jay cried, "Look!" and his gaze was frozen,

"Skip didn't choose—
but he
was chosen.

A hitchhiker seed is caught in his fur.
He's giving a ride
to a
cocklebur!"

We laughed and said, "Well, it goes to show

there's many a way for a seed to go.

Some fly.

34

Some pop when their pods unravel.

35

Some float.

37

Some drop to the grass and gravel.

38

Some go for a trip
on a dog like Skip.

41

It's hard to keep up with the way they travel!"

42